IF SANTA ONLY VISITS GOOD BOYS,
WILL WULLIE GET HIS GAMES AND TOYS?

WULLIE'S WEAPONS ARE RATHER ODD, A SNA' BA' AND A FISHING ROD.

AUCHENSHOOGLE HAS A SUDDEN SNOWFALL.

I'LL BE FIRST TAE PUT FOOTPRINTS ON THE NEW SNA'.

OCH! THE DELIVERY MAN HAS BEATEN ME TAE IT.

I'LL GIE HIM A SNA' BA'.

MISSED ME, WULLIE.

ZIIING!!

HOWL!

JINGS! IT HIT PC MURDOCH. I HOPE HE DIDNAE SEE ME.

THE FISHIN' SEASON IS OPEN. I'LL BE FIRST TAE CATCH A SALMON THIS YEAR.

HERE GOES.

WHIT IN THE NAME...

I KEN IT WAS YOU WI' THE SNOWBALL, AND NOW THIS. WHAT'S WRONG WI' YOU TH' DAY?

I JUST WANT TAE BE FIRST AT DAEIN' SOMETHING.

IS THAT A FACT? WELL, THE INSPECTOR GIED ME A BRAND NEW NOTEBOOK.

AND YOU'LL BE THE VERY FIRST NAME IN IT.

NAME, ADDRESS AND WHAUR DAE YE BIDE?

HUH! YOU KEN THAT OFF BY HEART.

THIS IS MAH FIRST BAD MOOD O' THE DAY.

MELT

BAD MOODS DINNA LAST LONG WI' OOR WULLIE. THEY DISAPPEAR LIKE SNA' AFF A BUCKET.

WHISTLE.

PRIMROSE CAN'T BELIEVE HER EYES, THAT DRIVER IS MOOSIE SIZE.

WULLIE'S GOING TAE MEET ME HERE TAE SHOW ME HIS NEW TOY.

I'LL HAE A SEAT ON HIS BUCKET AND WAIT ON HIM.

HELP MAH BOAB!

HA, HA, SOAPY! I MOVED THE BUCKET WI' MY NEW REMOTE CONTROL CAR.

I'M GLAD YOU THINK IT'S FUNNY.

I'VE PUT JEEMY IN THE CAR. IT LOOKS LIKE HE'S DRIVING IT.

WE COULD GIE PRIMROSE A RICHT FLEG WITH IT.

EEEEEEK! A MOUSE DRIVING A CAR! EEEEEEEEEEK!

HELP! POLICE! HELP!

HA! HA! WE'VE SENT PRIMROSE UP THE LAMP POST.

WHAT'S GOING ON 'ERE THEN?

CRUNCH!

I WANT THAT MOUSE ARRESTED FOR DANGEROUS DRIVING.

AW, PC MURDOCH, WE WERE ONLY HAVIN' A LAUGH. WHERE ARE YOU TAKING THEM?

THE CAR IS GOING TAE THE POLIS CAR POUND AND THE MOOSE TAE THE POLIS MOOSE POUND.

SHORTLY—

CAN WE BAIL THEM OOT, PLEASE?

PRIMROSE LEFT A CHARITY COLLECTING CAN WI' ME.

MAYBE IF YOU PAID SOME CASH INTAE THAT.

I'VE ONLY GOT A COUPLE O' BOB.

WELL, IT'S A SMALL CAR AND IT'S JEEMY'S FIRST OFFENCE.

PRIMROSE CHARITY BOX

JEEMY DISNAE LOOK ANY WORSE FOR BEING ARRESTED.

IF ONYTHING HE LOOKS FATTER.

I'M HAVIN' A CHEESE SANDWICH WITHOOT THE CHEESE. I FED IT A' TAE THAT WEE MOOSE.

FLOP!

WULLIE COULD FIND FAME AHEAD,
WITH THE HELP OF HIS AULD SHED.

TO HELP SCOTLAND WIN THE GAMES, IS ONE OF WULLIE'S MAJOR AIMS.

WULLIE'S ACT TURNS OUT A SCREAM,
AFTER HIS ASSISTANT'S DREAM.

WULLIE'S REHEARSIN' BURNS POETRY.

I'M RECITIN' 'TO A MOUSE' AT SCHOOL TOMORROW AND I'M TRAININ' JEEMIE TO ACT IT OOT AS I READ.

WEE SLEEKIT, COWERIN, TIM'ROUS BEASTIE, O, WHAT A PANIC'S IN THY BREASTIE!

YOU'VE TAE LOOK FEART WHEN I READ THAT, JEEMIE.

THOU NEED NA START AWA SAE HASTY...

THAT'S RICHT, RUN AWA' AT THAT BIT.

HAE SOME CHEESE THEN GET SOME SLEEP. WE'LL BE THE STAR O' THE SHOW TOMORROW.

EATIN' CHEESE TOO LATE MAKES JEEMIE DREAM.
MOOSE POWER!

HOI, WEE SLEEKIT COWERIN TIM'ROUS WULLIE.

YE'D BETTER RUN AWA FRAE ME SAE HASTY.

OCH! IT WAS A DREAM. BUT A BRAW DREAM.

NEXT DAY-
I WILL NOW RECITE 'TO A MOUSE' WHICH WILL BE ACTED OOT BY MY ASSISTANT JEEMIE.

MOOSE POWER!
OOYAH!
NIP!!

HOWL! THAT'S NO' IN THE POEM, YE WEE RODENT!
HA! HA!
HOP!

THE BEST LAID PLANS O' MICE AND MEN, GANG AFT A-GLEY.
JINGS!
HUFF!

IN WULLIE'S HOOSE ON BURNS NIGHT,
A HAGGIS MEAL, A TASTY DELIGHT.

WULLIE HOPES THAT NAEBODY SEES, HE'S NO WEARING DUNGAREES.

 HE'S NO' DRESSED YET.

 MA! WHERE'S MY DUNGAREES?

 BOTH PAIRS ARE IN THE WASH AND THE WASHING MACHINE IS BROKEN DOON. PUT ON YOUR TRACK SUIT. YE NEVER WEAR IT.

AW, JINGS!

 TRACK SUITS ARE THE VERY DAB FOR ACTIVE LADDIES LIKE YERSEL.

THIS IS AWFY!

 I CANNA LET BOB AND SOAPY SEE ME LIKE THIS. THEY'LL LAUGH AT ME.

 TIME TAE BE MA'S ACTIVE LADDIE.

 Boiiiig!

 I'LL HIDE IN NEXT DOOR'S BUSHES.

 NAE SIGN O' WULLIE.

HE'LL HAE SWEETIES HE DOESN'T WANT TAE SHARE.

PHEW! THEY'RE GOING. I'LL DISAPPEAR INTAE THE PARK NOW.

 OCH! HERE COMES PRIMROSE NOW. SHE'LL BE PLEASED. SHE'S NEVER LIKED MY DUNGAREES.

 I'LL SHIN UP THE TREE AND SHE'LL NEVER SPOT ME.

 THIS TEN YEAR AULD NEST WILL GET RID OF HER.

 URG! ROTTEN EGGS!

SPLAT!

 SOMEONE DUMPED ROTTEN EGGS ON ME FROM UP THAT TREE, PC MURDOCH.

UH-OH!

 I DINNA SEE ONYBODY.

YEE-HA! I'LL ESCAPE OWER THE TREES.

SWING! SWING!

 WELL, DID YE HAVE FUN IN YOUR TRACK SUIT, WULLIE?

AYE, MA. I DID.

 FUN TRYING NOT TAE BE SEEN IN IT. HA! HA!

WULLIE'S BUSINESS TO MAKE MONEY,
BECOMES A STORY THAT IS FUNNY.

IT'S ALMOST VALENTINE'S DAY - I'VE A BRAW MONEY-MAKING IDEA.

WULLIE'S Secret VALENTINE SERVICE

I'LL DELIVER VALENTINE CARDS FOR FOLK WHO ARE TOO SHY TO DO IT THEMSELVES.

COULD YOU DELIVER THIS TO MAGGIE BROON?

JINGS! AUCHENTOGLE IS A GOOD DISTANCE FROM AUCHENSHOOGLE.

I'LL PAY YOU FIVE POUNDS.

I'M ON MY WAY ALREADY.

10 GLEBE STREET. THIS IS EASY MONEY.

IS MAGGIE IN, MRS BROON?

SHE'S AWAY UP AT THE BUT AN' BEN, WULLIE.

MORE WORK, BUT HEY, A FIVER IS A LOT O' CASH.

THIS LOOKS LIKE A SHORTCUT BUT IT'S AWFY BOGGY.

HELP MAH BOAB! THE WIND'S CAUGHT THE CARD.

COME BACK TO WULLIE.

OCH! IT'S STUCK IN THE MUD.

AT LEAST NOW IT'S BLOWING TOWARDS THE BUT AN' BEN.

AHA! A CARD WI' MY NAME ON IT.

SHRIEK!

CROAK!

CRIVVENS! A PUDDOCK GOT INTO THE ENVELOPE.

LATER-

WHAT DID YOU DO? MAGGIE GAVE ME A SLAP AND SAID NEVER TO SPEAK TO HER AGAIN.

DOES THIS MEAN NO FIVER?

HE TOLD ME TO HOP IT. SIGH!

YOU JOIN US HERE IN WULLIE'S YARD FOR THE FINAL OF THE BUCKET JUMP.

SEVEN BUCKETS WILL BE A NEW PERSONAL BEST FOR WULLIE, THE SPIKY-HAIRED ATHLETE FROM TEAM AUCHENSHOOGLE.

CRIVVENS!

NOW MY FOOT'S STUCK.

STOP YOUR NONSENSE, WULLIE. WE'RE GOING TO BUY SCHOOL SHOES BEFORE THEY'RE SOLD OUT.

ARRGH! SHE SAID THE 'S' WORD!

YOU'VE NOT TO MENTION SCHOOL WHILE WE'RE ON HOLIDAYS.

YOU'LL BE BACK THERE IN A FORTNIGHT IN BARE FEET IF YOU DON'T HURRY.

CAN I TAKE ONE OF MY PALS FOR A SECOND OPINION?

AYE, BOB OR SOAPY BUT NOT THEM BOTH.

I'LL TAKE PRIMROSE.

WULLIE'S GONE NUTS.

OH, WILLIAM, DARLING.

DO GO IN HERE. IT'S THE BEST SHOE SHOP IN TOWN.

MUCH POSHER THAN I USUALLY GO TO.

YOU'D SUIT THESE SHOES, MA.

NONSENSE — I'M FAR TOO OLD FOR THEM.

NOT AT ALL — THEY WOULD SUIT YOU JUST SO WELL.

YOU THINK?

IS THAT MY SIZE?

YES, AND THE COLOUR IS TO DIE FOR.

I'M NOT NUTS AT ALL. I KNEW THIS WOULD HAPPEN.

NOW THAT MA HAS PRIMROSE SHE'LL NEVER NOTICE ME GONE.

HA! HA! THAT WAS A PERSONAL BEST SKIVE.

IS THIS WULLIE'S LUCKY DAY?
WITHOOT WORK HE'S GETTING PAY.

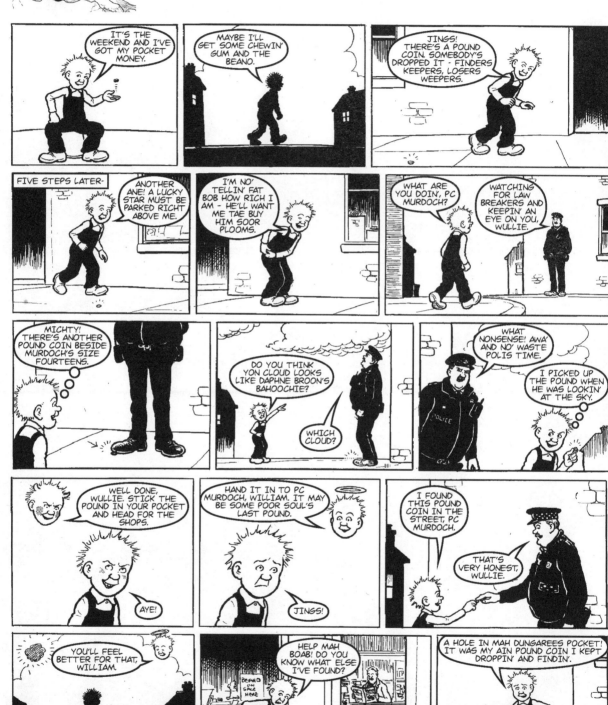

THIS STORY IS BY WAY OF A TOAST,
TO THE STAR WULL ADMIRES THE MOST.

EDITOR'S NOTE - TV PERSONALITY LORRAINE KELLY RECEIVES AN OBE IN THE 2012 NEW YEAR HONOURS LIST.

WULLIE AND BOAB ARE ON THE MAKE,
SELLING GOODS THAT ARE A FAKE.

WULLIE GIES THE BA' A SCUD, ON A PITCH THAT'S MAISTLY MUD.

WULLIE'S AWA PLAYING FITBA.

MESSI DRIBBLES THROUGH THE SCOTLAND DEFENCE. YOU CAN HEAR WEE GORDON STRACHAN GROAN.

ONLY WULLIE CAN SAVE SCOTLAND FROM DEFEAT IN THIS WORLD CUP FINAL!

OH, WILLIAM.

AYE?

WAGS AREN'T ALLOWED ON THE PITCH - AWA YE GO.

AM I YOUR GIRLFRIEND THEN?

NAW, I MEANT TAE SAY 'NAGS'.

NOW IT'LL TAKE ONE O' WULLIE'S FAMOUS TACKLES TO STOP MESSI.

AND HE'S DONE IT! FABULOUS PLAY BY THE YOUNG SCOTSMAN.

CRUNCH!

GUAN YERSEL! THE SPIKY HAIRED GENIUS SCORES ANITHER WONDER GOAL! SCOTLAND HAVE WON THE WORLD CUP!

YOU'RE A BRAW TACKLER BUT YOUR SHOOTING'S MINCE!

TALKING O' MINCE, IT MUST BE NEAR DENNER TIME.

I BET RONALDO DISNAE ASK GARETH BALE TAE DAE THIS.

WOOPS!

RIP!

WE'LL PLAY THE SECOND HALF EFTER DENNER SO DINNA HAE TOO MANY STOVIES, BOB.

WULLIE! LOOK AT YE - WHIT A STATE TAE COME HAME IN!

UH-OH. THIS COULD MEAN THE DREADED EARLY BATH...

AWA AND HAE A SHOWER THIS VERY MINUTE.

HUH! NO EVEN A YELLY CAIRD FIRST. SCOTLAND WANTS LADDIES TAE BE PLAYING FITBA IN THE PARK.

I'VE BEEN ON THE ROOF FOR HOURS BUT THAT'S THE GUTTERS CLEAN AT LAST.

WELL DONE, PA - YOU'RE MY HERO.

WHIT?

WELL DONE? WELL DONE? PA'S IN A WORSE STATE THAN I EVER WAS.

OCH, BUT WULLIE...

JINGS! IF I LIVE TAE BE A HUNNER I'LL STILL NEVER UNDERSTAND GROWN-UPS.

BEHIND WULLIE, IN HOT PURSUIT, PLODS A SIZE FOURTEEN BOOT.

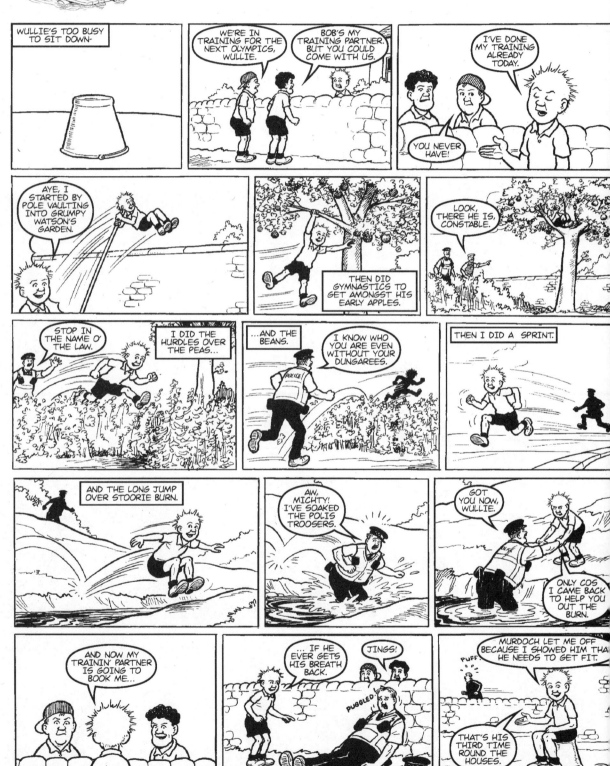

WULLIE'S TENT IS FULL O' FAULTS,
HE FIXES THEM BY DOING A WALTZ.

MA GAVE WULLIE AND BOB A POUND EACH.

AUCHENSHOOGLE CAR BOOT SALE-

WE'LL GIVE YOU TWA QUID FOR THAT TENT.

YOU'RE ROBBIN' ME BUT ON YE GO.

IT'S A BRAW TENT.

IT'S FULL O' HOLES. WE'VE WASTED OOR MONEY.

YOU'RE GUID AT SEWING, PRIMROSE. MEND THE HOLES IN OOR TENT.

IF YOU'LL DO SOMETHING FOR ME, WILLIAM.

HA! HA!

I LOVE BALLROOM DANCING.

STRICTLY TWA DANCES, MIND.

YOU LOOKED A PROPER PUDDEN, WULLIE.

IT'LL BE WORTH IT.

WE'LL GO CAMPIN' DOON ON THE BEACH.

TENT PEGS ARE EASY TO KNOCK INTO THE SAND.

HURRY, IT'S STARTIN' TAE RAIN.

TOLD YE IT WAS A GREAT TENT. WE'RE BONE DRY.

EXCEPT FOR THE TIDE COMIN' IN.

MY BOOTS ARE LEAKIN'.

IT'S OWER THE TOP O' MINE.

SPLOSH!

WOULD YOU BELIEVE IT - THE CAR HOOD HAS JAMMED.

OH, PERCIVAL! MY NEW DRESS WILL BE RUINED.

PUT OOR TENT UP IN THE BACK O' YOUR CAR, MISTER.

WHAT A BRILLIANT IDEA.

HE'S GIVEN US A RUN HAME AND A TENNER.

THE TENT TURNED OUT TAE BE A GRAND BUY AFTER A'.

WE'LL CAMP IN HERE TILL THE RAIN GOES AFF.

OR OOR MONEY RUNS OOT.

WULLIE'S OOT TAE IMPRESS, MARCHING IN HIS NATIONAL DRESS.

EDITOR'S NOTE – 2012 AND OOR WULLIE IS THE OFFICIAL MASCOT OF THE KILTWALK CHARITY
FOR A CAMPAIGN TO RAISE £1 MILLION FOR OOR KIDS.

NOW'S THE TIME TO STOP THE TALK,
NOW'S THE TIME TO WALK THE WALK.

WULLIE WILL RUN AS FAST AS HE'S ABLE, WHEN MINCE AND TATTIES ARE ON THE TABLE.

WULLIE'S DAY IS FULL O' FUN,
AND A VISIT FRAE THE EASTER BUN.

MICHTY! WULLIE'S LUGS HAVE GROWN.

THE EASTER BUNNY HAS COME TAE VISIT ME. THAT MUST BE LUCKY.

BREAKFAST, WULLIE!

I'LL HIDE YOU IN MY DUNGAREES FOR NOW.

WHERE'S THE PORRIDGE, MA?

IT'S BRAN FLAKES TODAY SO DINNA GO MAKING A FACE, JUST EAT THEM UP.

HEH! HEH! THE EASTER BUNNY IS EATING THEM FOR ME.

JINGS! THE BUNNY HAS POOED ON THE TABLE.

IS THAT CHOCOLATE RAISINS, SON? I'LL HAVE ANE.

NAW! THEY'RE ALL MINE.

YOU GREEDY WEE PIG! THAT'S NO' LIKE YOU, WULLIE.

SLAM!

YEACH! THAT WASN'T SO LUCKY - RABBIT POO ON MY HANDS.

WOULD YE LOOK AT THAT - THE EASTER BUNNY IS EXERCISING HARRY FOR ME.

WHOA - NO! THESE DAFFS WERE MA'S PRIDE AN' JOY.

BIDE UNDER THERE, BUNNY, TILL WULLIE THINKS WHAT TAE DO WITH YOU.

HAVE YOU SEEN A RABBIT RUNNING ABOOT, WULLIE? MOLLY'S WEE PET HAS ESCAPED.

AYE, THIS IS YOUR LUCKY DAY.

NAUGHTY CUDDLES.

THANKS, WULLIE. HERE'S SOME FLOOERS FOR YOUR MA.

THAT'LL MAKE UP FOR HER SQUASHED DAFFS.

OH, WULLIE. YOU'RE A WEE SMASHER.

HARRY GOT A DOGGY CHOC EGG. HAPPY EASTER, A'BODY.

BIG ECK REALLY IS THE PITS,
SMASHING WULLIE'S WORK TAE BITS.

HAPPY EASTER TAE ABODY.

I'VE MADE A BRAW BIG EASTER EGG OOT O' CLAY. NO' HALF BAD.

THAT EGG'LL NO' WIN THE COMPETITION, YE WEE SHRIMP.

JINGS! IT'S BIG ECK BLACK.

HOW DAE YE KNOW THAT?

BECAUSE IT'S A' SMASHED!

SMASH!

BIG BAP HEID! I'LL MARMELLISE YOU FOR THAT.

HA! HA! DAE AH LOOK WORRIED?

THERE'S MRS YOUNGER FRAE NEXT DOOR.

TAKE THAT DINOSAUR SUIT OFF, RYAN. YOU'RE OWER HOT.

CAN I BORROW THE SUIT FOR A WEE WHILE, RYAN?

AYE, IF YOU MAK' ME A CATAPULT LATER.

NOW I NEED HARRY.

WHISTLE!

THAT'S BRAW. BE A GOOD WEE DUG FOR WULLIE.

Wullie's SHED

DINNA POKE YER WET NOSE THROUGH THE PAPER YET.

EASTER EGG COMPETITION

WHIT'S THAT UGLY THING?

A DINOSAUR EGG.

THERE'S NAE SUCH A THING.

DINNA DAE THAT — IT'S ABOOT TAE HATCH.

BOOT!

OH, MAMMY!

SNARL!

WHAT DID I TELL YE?

CHASE HIM RICHT OOT O' THE PARK, HARRY.

HELP! IT'S A PREHYSTERICAL MONSTER!

WE GOT A CHOCCY EGG FOR GETTING RID O' BIG ECK.

I'LL EAT THE EGG AN' YOU CAN HAE MY MINCE AN' TATTIES, HARRY.

PECH!

FOR OOR WULLIE HAVE A CARE,
HIS LIFE'S BECOME A REAL NIGHTMARE.

THIS IS AWFY STRANGE – MY BUCKET IS MISSING.

MA'LL HAE BORROWED IT WITHOOT TELLING ME.
I HOPE YOUR FEET ARE CLEAN.

OCH, THIS IS A PLASTIC BUCKET.
STOP MAKING SIC A GUDDLE.

AHA! PA'S USING AN AULD TIN BUCKET – THAT'LL BE MINE.

NO, IT'S NOT! THIS ANE ISNAE COMFY LIKE MINE.
AYE, WELL – YOU CAN JIST GO AND FILL UP MY BUCKET WI' WATER AGAIN.

ONLY ONE THING FOR IT – GO AND SEE THE POLIS.

MICHTY! IT'S AL CAPONE COME TAE GIE HIMSELF UP.
I'M HERE TAE REPORT A MISSING PERSON, PC MURDOCH.

GIE ME A DESCRIPTION.
ONE FOOT TALL. GREY COMPLEXION, IN FACT APPEARS TO BE A LITTLE PAIL.

THIS IS YOUR BUCKET – NO' A REAL PERSON.
BUT MY BUCKET IS MY BEST FRIEND. HE KEEPS ME COMPANY WHEN I'M LONELY, BEEN A HELMET WHEN I'M ATTACKED. I TELL HIM A' MY SECRETS AND HE NEVER LETS ME DOON.

MURDOCH SAID I WAS WASTIN' VALUABLE POLIS TIME. HUH! IT WOULD BE DIFFERENT IF HE HAD LOST HIS FAVOURITE HANDCUFFS.

WHAT A DAY.

I'LL HAE A WEE SIT DOON AND RECOVER.

MICHTY! I FORGOT MAH BUCKET'S GONE.
THUD!

YOU'VE GOT TAE HELP ME, READERS. IF YOU SPOT MY BUCKET SEND ME A PHOTIE OR SOMETHING TAE LET ME KNOW HE'S OKAY.

WHEN WULLIE'S BUCKET CAN'T BE FOUND,
AUCHENSHOOGLE RALLIES ROUND.

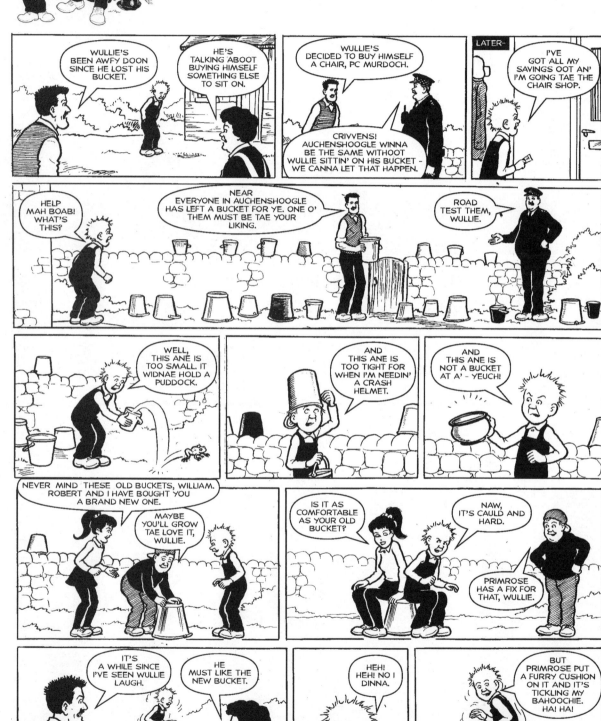

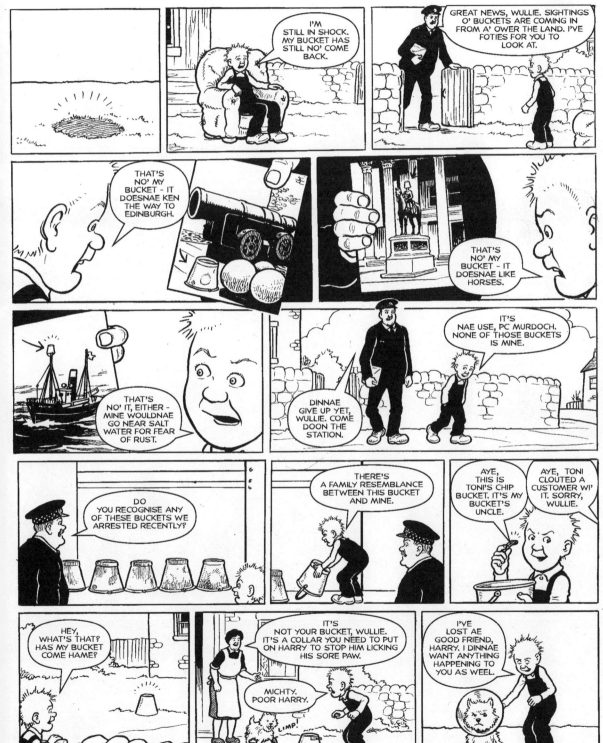

TRYING TAE FIND HIS AIN DEAR SEAT,
IS ENOUGH TAE MAK' OOR WULLIE GREET.

WITH MAH BUCKET MISSING I'VE NO' HAD A DECENT SEAT IN WEEKS.

NOTEBOOK, PENCIL AND TWA WEDGES OF CHEESE. I'M GOING OOT TAE LOOK FOR MY BUCKET LIKE A PROPER POLIS MAN.

I'LL PARK UP ON STOORIE BRAE AND WATCH FOR SUSPICIOUS BUCKETS. LIKE THE POLIS CARS DAE ON THE MOTORWAY.

JEEMIE THE MOOSE.

IT WAS A BRAINWAVE TAE USE CHEESE WEDGES TAE CHOCK MAH WHEELS.

DID I HEAR THE WORD CHEESE?

I'M NO' LETTING THIS BRAW CHEDDAR LIE ABOOT.

CRIVVENS! I'M ON THE MOVE.

CHOCKS AWAY, WULLIE! SQUEEK! SQUEEK!

AAARGH! IT'S CAULD!

SPLASH!

AND I DINNA HAVE A BUCKET TAE BALE OOT WITH.

NAE BUCKET AND NOW NAE CARTIE, BOB.

I'VE GOT SOMETHING THAT'LL REPLACE BOTH YER BUCKET AND YER CARTIE. I'LL DRIVE IT ROOND TAE YOUR SHED, WULLIE.

MY AULD SPACE HOPPER.

IF IT TAKES YOUR WEIGHT, IT MUST BE STRONG.

I'LL GIE IT A GO.

UH-OH! WULLIE'S PENCIL.

HELP MAH BOAB! I'M PUNCTURED.

WOOOOSH!

OUCH!

CRASH!

NO MORE SEARCHIN' FOR MY BUCKET. I'M FINISHED WI' THEM. NEXT WEEK I'M BUYING A PROPER CHAIR.

JINGS, WULLIE! FOWK WILL NO' RECOGNISE YOU ANY MAIR.

WULLIE THINKS IT REALLY GREAT,
THE HELP HE GETS FRAE HIS MATE.

WULLIE LANDS IN POLIS TROUBLE, AND NOW HE'S STARTED SEEING DOUBLE.

WULLIE IS GIVEN A BRAW BLACK EYE, FRAE A WARRIOR THAT CALLS HIM 'SWEETIE PIE'.

WULLIE'S AWAY TO HIS KARATE CLASS.

GOT YE, BOB.

CHEATER! I WASN'T READY.

THAT'S ENOUGH FOR TONIGHT, LADS.

CRUMP!

ARE YOU WALKING HOME, BOYS?

NO, WE'RE WAITING FOR MY MAW TO PICK US UP.

ARE YOU NO' SCARED? IT'S REALLY DARK TONIGHT, WULLIE?

SCARED, ME? I'M THE TOUGHEST LADDIE IN AUCHENSHOOGLE. YOU SAW HOW EASY I THREW YOU.

MAYBE YOU TWO SHOULD GO TO KNITTING OR FLOWER ARRANGING CLASSES.

HUH!

IF ANYBODY ATTACKS ME, I'LL BE READY FOR THEM.

JINGS! SORRY, MATE. I DIDN'T SEE YOU THERE.

EEEEK!

THUMP!

SO YOU WANT TO MAKE SOMETHING O' THIS - I SAID I'M SORRY.

THUMP!

WHACK!!

HELP MAH BOAB! WHAT HIT ME?

GULP!

I DIDN'T REALLY THINK THERE WERE NINJA WARRIORS IN AUCHENSHOOGLE.

NEXT DAY.

HOW DID YOU GET THE BLACK EYE, WULLIE?

WERE YOU ATTACKED LAST NIGHT?

AYE, BUT IT TOOK A TRAINED NINJA WARRIOR TO DO IT.

SORRY I HIT YOU LAST NIGHT, WILLIAM. I HAD JUST BEEN TO MY SELF DEFENCE CLASSES AND I THINK I GOT CARRIED AWAY.

PRIMROSE?

LET ME KISS IT BETTER.

GET OFF, WOMAN.

HA! HA! WARRIOR INDEED!

BLOOMIN' PRIMROSE - I GOT BOTH A BLACK EYE AND A RED FACE FROM HER.

NEVER A DAY SEEMS TO PASS,
WITHOOT WULL KEPT BEHIND IN CLASS.

THE LANG ARM O' THE LAW GIES WULLIE A HAND, LOOKING EFTER HIS AIN BIT LAND.

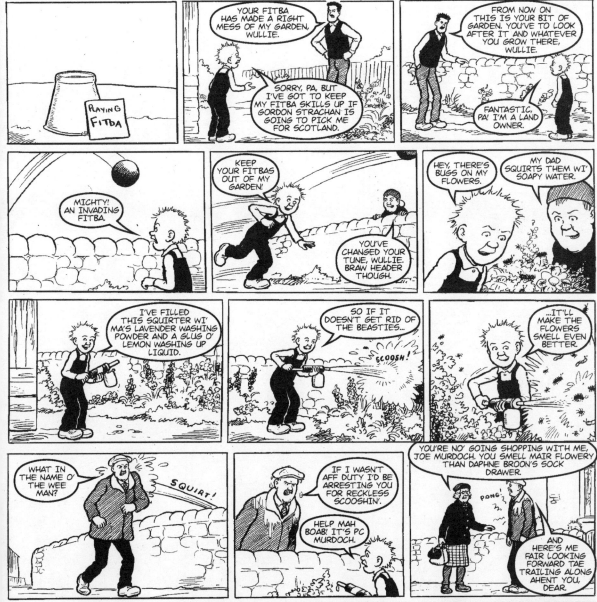

WULLIE'S RUNNING AT THE DOUBLE, TAE KEEP HIS PAL OOT O' TROUBLE.

THE FISHING SEASON HAS STARTED.

THE TROOT IN THIS RIVER HAVEN'T WOKEN UP YET. LET'S GO AND FISH THE FAR LOCH.

WE'LL NEED TO GET A PERMIT OR THON GRUMPY AULD GAMIE WILL CATCH US.

SO—

PERMITS FOR THE FAR LOCH ARE TWO POUNDS EACH, WULLIE.

WE HAVE TO KEEP TWO POUNDS FOR LATER, MIND.

THIS IS MAIR LIKE IT.

FISHING BY PERMIT ONLY

WOW! I'VE GOT A BEAUTY.

ME TOO.

WHAT'S THIS? POACHING ON MY LOCH, EH?

THE GAMIE!

YOU NEED A PERMIT TO FISH HERE.

IS THAT A FACT?

COME BACK HERE, YE SCOUNDREL.

NOT LIKELY.

GRAB!

JINGS! HE'S A QUICK MOVER FOR AN AULD GAMIE.

NAEBODY FISHES MY LOCH WITHOUT A PERMIT. I'M CALLING THE POLIS.

I'VE GOT A PERMIT.

WHAT'S THAT YE SAY?

WHY DID YE RUN OFF WHEN YOU HAD A PERMIT?

TO LET THE OTHER LAD GET AWAY. WE COULD ONLY AFFORD ANE.

THE GAMIE'S FACE MUST HAVE BEEN A PICTURE.

AYE, HE WAS FAIR SCUNNERED.

I'LL AWAY TAE TONI'S FOR TWO POUNDS WORTH O' CHIPS, WULLIE.

THEN WE'LL GIVE OOR MOTHERS A RARE FISH TEA FOR MOTHER'S DAY.

OOR YOUNG SHERLOCK'S ON THE CASE, BUT IS HE LOOKIN' IN THE RIGHT PLACE?

WULLIE'S AWA' OOT-

HEH! HEH! MURDOCH'S POLIS CAR IS REALLY DIRTY.

CREEP!

HE CANNAE SEE ME.

PLEESE CLEAN ME

LATER-

I KEN IT WAS YOU WHO WROTE ON MAH CAR.

HOW DO YOU KNOW?

BECAUSE I'M A BRAW DETECTIVE AND YOU'RE A ROTTEN SPELLER.

I FANCY BEING A DETECTIVE LIKE SHERLOCK HOLMES.

MICHTY! MY BUCKET'S BEEN PINCHED.

A FOOTPRINT! SOMEBODY JUMPED OWER THE WA' TAE GET MY BUCKET.

FAT BOB CANNAE JUMP. SOAPY HAS A RASH. LANKY LAIRD IS THE BEST JUMPER IN OOR SCHOOL.

THERE'S A BUCKET IN LANKY'S YARD. IT MICHT BE MINE.

MY BUCKET HAS A RED PENT MARK INSIDE. I'LL TAK' A LOOK.

YE WEE SCUNNER! YE'VE LET MY PUDDOCK COLLECTION ESCAPE!

I'LL BOOT YER BACKSIDE FOR THAT, WULLIE!

HELP! MURDER! POLIS!

JINGS! MAH BUCKET'S WI' PC MURDOCH

AYE, HELPIN' TAE WASH YOUR WRITIN' AFF MY CAR. A DETECTIVE WID SURELY WORK THAT OOT.

HUH! HE EVEN WASHED YOU TOO, YE WEE TRAITOR!

**WULLIE AND HIS SOJER BOYS,
ALLOW NAE LASSIES IN THEIR PLOYS.**

WE'RE STARTIN' THE SCHOOL PLAY TODAY.

TO KEEP YOU ALL HAPPY I'M GOING TO APPOINT THE MOST POPULAR BOY IN THE CLASS TO DIRECT OUR PLAY...

...STEP FORWARD, WILLIAM!

THANK YOU, THANK YOU...

HOORAY! WULLIE'S THE BEST.

WAHEY!

WE'RE DOING SNOW WHITE SO I'LL GIVE YOU ALL YOUR PARTS.

BOB, YOU CAN PLAY DOPEY.

WHIT? ARE YOU TRYING TAE SAY I'M THICK?

I'M NO' SPEAKING TAE WULLIE.

IT WASNAE A SPEAKIN' PART ONYWAY.

PRIMROSE, YOU'LL BE THE WICKED QUEEN.

YOU CANNOT BE SERIOUS, WILLIAM.

I MUST BE SNOW WHITE FOR I AM THE PRETTIEST.

AND YOU'RE AYE LOOKING IN THE MIRROR TAE SEE IF YOU ARE - JUST LIKE THE WICKED QUEEN.

SOAPY, YOU'LL BE THE PRINCE AND KISS SNOW WHITE BACK TO LIFE.

ONLY IF PRIMROSE IS SNOW WHITE.

WELL SHE'S NO'! CHERYL GLUMFER IS SNOW WHITE.

I'M NO' KISSIN' HER - SHE LOOKS LIKE A FROG.

ARE YOU GOING TAE LET HIM TALK TAE ME LIKE THAT?

CHERYL.

SHE SHOULD BE GRUMPY.

NAG! NAG! NAG! NAG! NAG! NAG! NAG! NAG! NAG! NAG! NAG! NAG! NAG! NAG!

ENOUGH! CUT! CUT! THAT'S IT FOR THE DAY.

CRIVVENS! I STARTED OOT THE MOST POPULAR LAD AND ENDED UP WI' NAEBODY SPEAKIN' TAE ME.

YOU REALLY HAVE TO GIVE A LAUGH,
WULL'S CAUGHT OOT BY HIS AUTOGRAPH.

WULLIE'S AT SCHOOL—

EVERY ANSWER IS WRONG IN YOUR ENGLISH TEST, WILLIAM.

AND YOUR WRITING IS SO BAD I COULD HARDLY READ THEM. DO IT AGAIN TONIGHT.

I'LL STILL GET A' THE ANSWERS WRONG.

THEN—

I'M NOT DOING IT ANYWAY. I'M WATCHING FITBA ON THE TELLY TONIGHT.

YOU'LL BE FOR IT AT SCHOOL TOMORROW, WULLIE.

THIS AULD TELLY IS ON THE BLINK. THANK GOODNESS OUR NEW WIDESCREEN IS BEING DELIVERED TOMORROW.

OCH! WE CAN'T SEE THE FITBA.

NEXT MORNING—

YOU'LL HAVE TO GET YOURSELF TO SCHOOL. PA'S AWAY TO WORK AND I'M OFF TO SEE AUNT JESSIE.

NO PROBLEM. I'LL JUST FINISH MY PORRIDGE.

HEH! HEH! I'LL BUNK OFF SCHOOL AND SAY I WAS TOO ILL TO DO MY HOMEWORK.

I WONDER WHO THIS IS?

KNOCK!

IT'S OOR NEW TELLY. CAN YOU LEAVE IT ON THE STEP?

AYE, IF YOU SIGN FOR IT, LADDIE.

NO BOTHER. I DINNA WANT YOU TO TAKE IT AWAY.

SCRIBBLE!

MA WILL BE HOME SOON. I'LL HIDE IN MY SHED TILL SCHOOL FINISHES.

WULLIE'S Shed

HELLO, WULLIE. I'M SURPRISED THEY LEFT THE TELLY WITHOOT SOMEBODY SIGNING FOR IT.

AYE, IMAGINE.

SORRY, SON. THE BOSS CAN'T READ YOUR WRITING. WILL YOU SIGN FOR IT AGAIN?

SO YOU WERE NOT AT SCHOOL, YOUNG MAN.

I'M SORRY BUT WULLIE WAS PLAYING TRUANT TODAY, MISS JONES.

BETTER LATE THAN NEVER. HE CAN STAY NOW AND DO HIS WRITING EXERCISE.

I MUST IMPROVE MY WRITING
I MUST IMPROVE MY WRITING
I MUST

AND I MUST DO THIS SO I DINNA GET CAUGHT OUT AGAIN.

AND I'M NOT GETTING TO SEE THE NEW TELLY FOR A WEEK.

WULLIE'S BEEN A GOOD LAD SINCE,
HE MISSED OOT ON A PLATE O' MINCE.

YOO-HOO, WULLIE!

THAT SOUNDS LIKE KATHY CARTNEY FRAE OWER THE ROAD.

WULLIE, YOU'RE GOOD WITH ANIMALS AND THINGS. WILL YOU LOOK AFTER ROCKY TODAY?

JINGS, HARRY MIGHT NO' LIKE ANOTHER DUG, MRS C.

NO, ROCKY IS OOR PARROT. I'VE PUT HIM IN THIS WEE TRAVEL CAGE.

YOO-HOO, WULLIE.

THAT'LL BE NAE BOTHER THEN.

I'LL WATCH THE FITBA WHILE I'M WATCHING ROCKY.

MICHTY! AUCHENSHOOGLE HAE LOST ANOTHER GOAL. WHAT A LOAD O' TRIPE!

HOI, MISTER! SWITCH OFF THAT TELLY AND GET YOUR HOMEWORK DONE WHILE I MAKE THE TEA.

BUT, MAW – IT'S ONLY HALF TIME.

I'LL SNEAK OOT THE BACK DOOR AND WATCH THE SECOND HALF AT BOB'S HOOSE.

CREEP!

WHAT DO YOU FANCY FOR TEA, WULLIE?

A LOAD O' TRIPE!

WULLIE, YOU DINNA LIKE TRIPE... OCH! IT'S THE BIRD! THE WEE RASCAL HAS ESCAPED.

GONE!

LOAD O' TRIPE.

MA'S BEEN COOKING SO SHE'S NO MISSED ME.

WHAT'S FOR TEA, MA?

JUST WHAT YOU ASKED FOR WHEN I SHOUTED THROUGH TO YOU.

A BRAW PLATE O' TRIPE.

WHIT? OH, ER...BRAW!

GROOOOO!

RUG! TUG! CHEW!

I WAS SURPRISED WHEN YOU WANTED TRIPE, WULLIE, BUT IT WAS YOUR VOICE.

IT MUST HAE BEEN THE PARROT.

WE'RE JUST HAVING MINCE AND TATTIES WI' PEAS.

YOU'RE NO' THE ONLY BIRD BRAIN HERE, ROCKY.

I'M ANE TOO.

THERE'S NAE MONSTERS IN THE DARK,
EXCEPT MAYBE THE STOORIE SHARK.

WULLIE'S AT SCHOOL.

WE'RE RECYCLING CANS TO MAKE MONEY FOR THE SCHOOL. THE PUPIL WHO COLLECTS MOST CAN HAVE A HALF DAY ON FRIDAY.

RECYCLING

THAT'S FOR ME!

DINNA YOU BE SO SURE.

LATER—

I'M NEEDING YOUR EMPTY CANS, MA.

SORRY, WULLIE - I RECYCLED THEM A'READY.

I'LL SEE IF THERE'S ONY IN THIS BIN?

WE'LL GIVE YE A HAND TAE LOOK, WULLIE.

HOWL!

SOMETHING SMELLS BAD AROOND HERE, BOB.

AYE, SOAPY - IT'S WULLIE!

YOU CHEATERS!

I HOPE YOU'RE NO' THINKING O' STARTING TAE DRINK BEER, WULLIE.

DINNA BE DAFT. I'M WAITING FOR THESE LADS TAE FINISH THEIR CANS.

LET ME TELL YOU WHERE I WAS ON DUTY LAST NICHT...WHISPER.

JINGS!

WE'RE GETTING TONS O' CANS. WHAUR ARE YOU GOING, WULLIE?

FARMER GRAY'S FIELD.

HA! HA! DAE YE THINK HIS COOS ARE DRINKING COLA?

PC MURDOCH TOLD ME THERE WAS A ROCK CONCERT HERE LAST NIGHT AND THEY HADNAE GOT ROUND TAE PICKING UP THE LITTER YET.

NEXT DAY—

STAND ASIDE FOR MY FIRST LOAD O' CANS.

I DINNA BELIEVE MY EYES.

MICHTY! HE'S GOT A MOUNTAIN O' THEM.

WILLIAM WINS THE HALF HOLIDAY FOR HIS SUPER RECYCLING EFFORT.

SMUG

MUTTER!

ENJOY SCHOOL, BOYS - THIS IS THE SORT OF CYCLING I'M DOING THIS AFTERNOON.

FUME!

HA! HA! DID YE SEE THEIR FACES?

YE CANNAE STOP OOR WULLIE GRINNIN',
THE SCHOOL HOLIDAYS ARE JUST BEGINNIN'.

TWICE A DAY THE SURFERS ARE MERRY, THANKS TAE THE PASSING O' THE FERRY.

THE LADS DECIDE TAE MAKE SOME LOOT,
USING UP THE SUMMER FRUIT.

WULLIE THINKS HE CAN GO FAR, BECOMING A GREAT FITBA STAR.

WULLIE SEES TROUBLE LOOM,
HE'S KICKED THE BA' INTAE MA'S BEST ROOM.

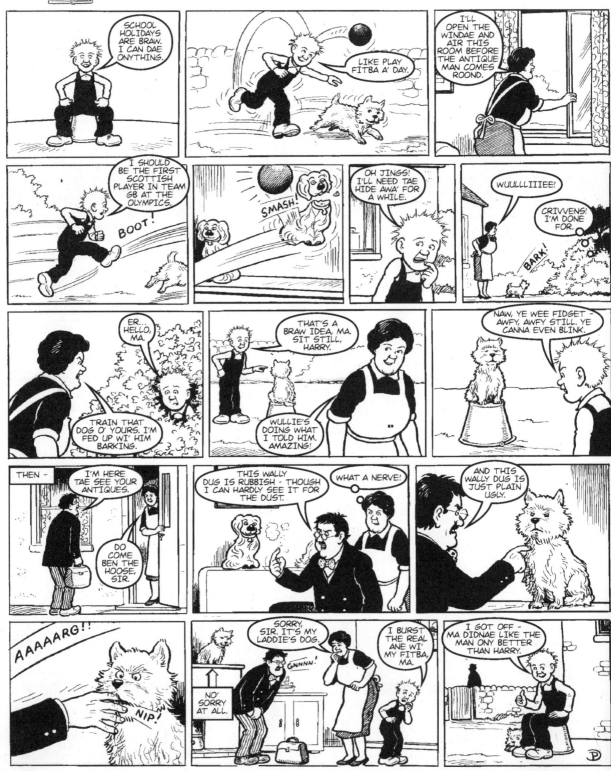

THERE'S NAE FISH IN THE BROOK,
UNTIL FAT BOB TAKES A DOOK.

 FAT BOB AN' ME WERE GOING TO GO TO THE BEACH.

BUT SINCE IT WAS RAINING LAST WEEK THE RIVER WILL BE BRAW FOR FISHING.

 THE SCHOOL'S ONLY BEEN OFF A WEEK AND YOU'VE NEAR EATEN ME OOT O' HOOSE AND HAME.

DINNA WORRY - I'LL BRING HOME THE TEA.

 SOON-

I'M HERE FIRST SO I GET THE BEST SPOT.

 SUMMER FISHING CANNA BE RUSHED.

 THE TROOT MUST THINK YOU'RE ON HOLIDAY. NO' A SKILLED HUNTER READY TO PUT HIM AMONGST SOME CHIPS.

 HELP MAH BOAB! A MONSTER!

 SPLASH!

 THE HOOK'S BEEN TAKEN RICHT AFF MY LINE. IT MUST HAE BEEN ENORMOUS.

 I'LL BE IN THE SUNDAY POST IF I CATCH A TWA TON FISH.

 THE TWA TON MONSTER - FAT BOB.

SILLY WULLIE. I JUST NICKED HIS HOOK COS I FORGOT TAE BRING ONY.

 HERE'S WULLIE'S LINE AGAIN. I'LL GIE HIM ANOTHER DOOKIN.

YANK!

 HOI, WHAT ARE YOU DOIN' HAULIN' IN MY LINE?

JINGS! WRANG LINE. IT'S THE GLAIKIT GAMEY.

 GLAIKIT, AM I? GET OOT O' HERE, YOU WEE POACHER.

GLUB!

SHOVE!

 SO IT WAS YOU MESSIN' ABOOT WITH MY LINE?

 YOU'RE FLOPPIN ABOOT LIKE A FISH OUT O' WATER, BOB.

I'LL SHOW YE WHY.

 THERE'S A MUCKLE TROOT IN MY WADERS.

I'LL SWOP YOU FOR THE HOOK YOU PINCHED.

 WE'RE FRYING TONIGHT, MA.

YE WEE DARLIN', WULLIE.

 THAT WAS BRAW. IF I ATE ANY MORE I'D BE THE SIZE O' FAT BOB.

WULLIE AND HIS PALS ARE FEELING MERRY,
THEY'RE AFF TAE GET THE LAST STRAWBERRY.

SWIMMING IN SCOTLAND'S SEAS,
MICHT WELL MAK' A BODY FREEZE.

I'M GOING SWIMMING.

I CANNA TAKE YOU SWIMMING, WULLIE. I'M VISITING CASTLES WI' MY HISTORY SOCIETY.

IT'S OWER PRICEY, THE SWIMMING ANYWAY. GO AND PLAY WITH YOUR PALS.

SO MUCH FOR THE SWIMMING, SOAPY.

MY GRANDAD SAYS THEY SWIM IN THE SEA A' YEAR ROOND IN BROUGHTY FERRY.

HIDE BEHIND THE SEAT AND WE'LL GET A FREE RIDE TAE BROUGHTY FERRY.

IT'S LIKE I TELT YE. THEY CALL THEM THE ANCIENT AMPHIBEANS.

THEY'RE CERTAINLY ANCIENT. IF THEY CAN DO IT, SO CAN WE.

AARGH!

IT'S FREEZING!

I'M TURNING TAE ICE.

I CANNA FEEL MY KNEES.

HA! HA! CHEERIO, YE YOUNG SOFTIES!

BRRRR!

WE'LL NEED TO FIND SOMEWHERE WARM TO CHANGE.

AYE OR WE'LL PERISH IN BROUGHTY FERRY AND NAEBODY WILL KNOW WE'RE HERE.

YOU'LL FREEZE, LADDIES. THE FIRE'S ON IN THE PUB, COME IN AND WARM YERSELS - WE'RE NO' OPEN FOR FIFTEEN MINUTES YET.

WE'RE SAVED.

THIS IS BRAW.

I'M GETTING HUNGRY. PITY WE DINNA HAVE ANY MONEY.

HA! HA!

WAIT A MINUTE. I KEN THAT LAUGH.

PA - SO MUCH FOR YOUR HISTORY SOCIETY.

WELL, ER... THIS PUB IS CALLED THE BROUGHTY CASTLE. AHEM!

FISH AND CHIPS. THANKS PA.

WELL, SON - US BLOKES HAVE TAE STICK TOGETHER.

I'VE NO' TAE SAY ANYTHING TAE MA.

WULLIE LOVES HAVIN' WORK TAE DO,
IN THE SHED WI' PAPER AND GLUE.

IS THIS A NEW LOOK FOR OOR WULLIE?
NAW, NAW, DINNA BE SILLY.

HI, FOLKS.

HELLO, WULLIE.

HI, SUSAN.

HI, WULLIE.

HI, MATH.

YOU MUST BE THE BEST KNOWN FACE IN THIS TOON.

YOU'RE AN AUCHENSHOOGLE CELEBRITY.

I SUPPOSE SO.

DO YOU WANT OOR WULLIE TAE OPEN YOUR NEW CAFE?

IT'LL ONLY COST YOU THREE BIG SLAP-UP SUPPERS.

I DINNA WANT THAT MUCKY WEE LADDIE ANYWHERE NEAR MY CAFE. HE COULD START A HEALTH SCARE.

YAH! YOUR CHIPS ARE SOGGY!

MAYBE YOU COULD OPEN MY MOTHER'S NEW BEAUTY SALON.

SHE WOULDN'T WANT A SCRUFFY GUY LIKE ME.

NAW, NAW - SCRUFFY'S GOOD.

PLUMP ROBERT IS RIGHT. YOU ARE PERFECT, WILLIAM.

EH? ARE YOU FEELIN' OKAY, MRS PATTERSON?

REMEMBER THE FEE, WULLIE.

SCRUB!

FIRST A LITTLE TIDY UP.

SCRAPE!

BRUSH!

THIS IS A TORTURE CHAMBER.

LADIES, YOU ALL KNOW WILLIAM, AUCHENSHOOGLE'S SCRUFFIEST BOY.

IF I CAN MAKE HIM LOOK LIKE THIS, THINK OF WHAT I COULD DO FOR YOU.

WE GOT TWO QUID FOR YOUR APPEARANCE.

SPEAK TAE US, WULLIE. IT COULDN'T HAVE BEEN THAT BAD.

HI, ECK.

WHO ARE YOU?

NO' THAT BAD? I'M SO POLISHED UP NAEBODY RECOGNISES ME NOW!

RUN! HE'S WANTIN' TAE ALTER OOR LOOKS.

PHEW! A CHASE OVER STOORIE BRAE AND A FECHT AND I'M BACK LOOKIN' NORMAL AGAIN.

FAMED FOR SPEED FAT BOB IS NOT,
ESPECIALLY WHEN THE WEATHER'S HOT.

THE FAMILY SHOULD COME TO NO HARM, NOW WULLIE'S MADE A BURGLAR ALARM.

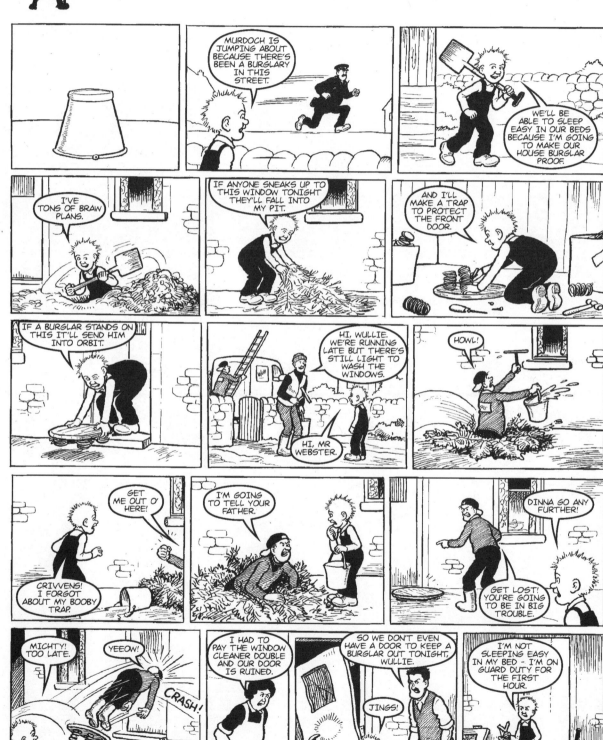

**OOR WULLIE'S VERY QUICK AT WALKING,
AND JUST AS FAST WHEN IT COMES TO TALKING.**

OCH! HERE COMES THAT PEST PRIMROSE PATERSON.

WILL YOU WALK THE EDINBURGH WEE KILTWALK WITH ME, WILLIAM?

NO, I'M WALKING IT WITH HARRY.

BUT YOU'RE MY BEST PAL, WILLIAM.

I'M CALLED WULLIE AND I'VE ALREADY PACKED CHEESE AND JEELY PIECES FOR HARRY AND ME.

I'VE MADE SOME CHOCOLATE BROWNIES FOR THE WALK. HMM! THEY'RE STILL WARM.

BROWNIES? YES, PLEASE.

HA! HA! LOOK AT HARRY, HE'S GOING TO WALK WITH ME ANYWAY.

HAIRY WEE TRAITOR!

MURRAYFIELD.

I'M GOING TO WALK WITH ONE OF MY FAMILY.

PLEASE YERSEL'.

CHRIS PATERSON – HE'S A SCOTTISH RUGBY GOD.

HI, COUSIN CHRIS.

COUSIN PRIMROSE.

I'M OOR WULLIE – PRIMROSE'S BEST PAL. I'M WALKING WITH YOU TAE.

MY SOMETIMES BEST PAL.

OFF WE GO THEN, WALKERS.

WE CAN HAVE A BRAW CHAT, CHRIS.

REALLY!

HOW MANY TIMES DID YOU PLAY FOR SCOTLAND? WHAT'S YOUR BEST POSITION? COULD YOU GET ME PICKED FOR SCOTLAND?

...WHO'S YOUR FAVOURITE PLAYER? WILL SCOTLAND BEAT SOUTH AFRICA NEXT MONTH?...

SAVE SOME BREATH FOR WALKING, WULLIE.

...AYE, BUT WHAT SIZE OF SHIRT DO YOU TAKE?...

...DO YOU EAT JEELY PIECES WHEN YOU'RE TRAINING? CAN YOU SING FLOWER O' SCOTLAND REALLY LOUD?...

...I'D MAKE A BRAW FLY HALF BECAUSE A'BODY SAYS I'M NO' HALF FLY. DO YOU THINK SO?

SIGH!

WHEN WE FINISHED THE WALK CHRIS SAID HE HAD SORE EARS.

FUNNY, YOU'D HAVE THOUGHT IT WOULD HAVE BEEN HIS FEET.

ZZZ

WULLIE'S FEELING IN THE 'PINK', MA SAYS IT'S TOO MUCH FIZZY DRINK.

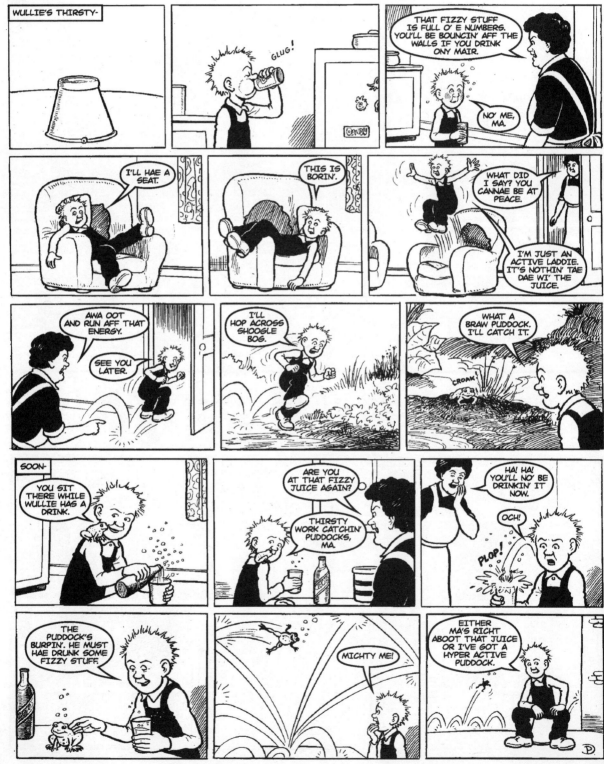

FOR HOTEL WORK WULL SHOULD BE ABLE,
FEET ON THE FLOOR AND NO' ON THE TABLE.

IF THE OLDIES WERE MAIR SKILLED THAN PLAYERS TODAY, WHY IS THAT FOOTBALL FLOATING AWAY?

THERE'S A LAD WULLIE LOVES TAE HATE, HIS AULD ENEMY, GINGER TAIT.

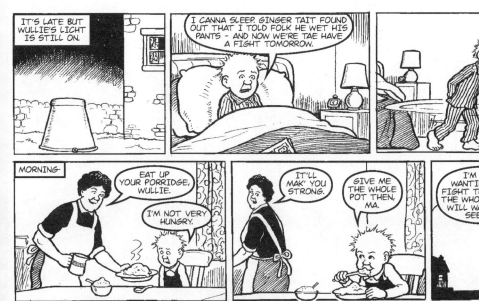

IT'S LATE BUT WULLIE'S LICHT IS STILL ON.

I CANNA SLEEP. GINGER TAIT FOUND OUT THAT I TOLD FOLK HE WET HIS PANTS - AND NOW WE'RE TAE HAVE A FIGHT TOMORROW.

THEY SAY HE'S AWFY TOUGH FOR AN AULD LAD - HE'S NEARLY ELEVEN.

PACE!

MORNING.

EAT UP YOUR PORRIDGE, WULLIE.

I'M NOT VERY HUNGRY.

IT'LL MAK' YOU STRONG.

GIVE ME THE WHOLE POT THEN, MA.

I'M NOT WANTING TAE FIGHT TODAY BUT THE WHOLE CLASS WILL WANT TAE SEE IT.

I'LL HIDE IN THE AULD TUNNEL AND SAY I GOT LOST.

OOR WULLIE!

GINGER TAIT!

YOU'RE HIDING FROM ME.

I'M NO' WANTING TAE FIGHT YOU.

USE MUD TAE GIVE OURSELVES BLACK EYES AND WE'LL SAY WE'VE HAD OOR FIGHT.

HEH! HEH! THIS IS A BRAW IDEA.

YOU CAN ALL GO HOME. WE'VE HAD OOR FIGHT.

LOOK AT OOR BLACK EYES.

WHIT? WE'VE BEEN WAITING HERE IN THE CAULD TO SEE THIS FIGHT.

TAKE THAT FOR LETTIN' US DOWN.

AND THAT! PAIR O' SPOILSPORTS!

WHACK!

BAM!

BIFF!

THESE BLACK EYES ARE REAL. SOME DAYS YOU JUST CANNAE WIN.

OF ALL THE PALS THAT WULLIE'S GOT,
THE BEST YIN IS HIS BIG ROBOT.

FAT BOB'S ON HIS WAY.

FANCY A GAME O' BOOLS, WULLIE?

AYE, WE'VE NO PLAYED THAT IN AGES.

HERE COMES MAH STEELIE.

I'M STILL WINNIN'.

CRIVVENS!

VROOM

DO YOU LIKE MY REMOTE CONTROL MODEL? IT CAN GO ANYWHERE.

IT'S SNOBBY PERCY PERKINS.

I'D GIVE YOU A SHOT BUT MUMMY SAID NOT TO PLAY WITH YOU TWO.

YOU CHAPS COULD NEVER AFFORD A MODEL LIKE THIS.

HUH! WE'VE A BIGGER REMOTE CONTROL MODEL THAN YOURS.

WHAUR'S OOR BIG MODEL, WULLIE?

WE DINNA HAE ANE YET, YE TUMSHIE!

WE'LL TURN YOU INTAE A REMOTE CONTROL ROBERT.

HEH! HEH!

I AM A ROBOT.

MY BUCKET MAK'S A BRAW HEID.

I'M SENDING MY ROBOT STRAIGHT AHEAD, PERCY.

GASP! IT'S HUGE.

I SHALL NOW TURN MY REMOTE CONTROL ROBOT AROUND.

GOSH!

WASP!

WULLIE, THERE'S A WASP COME IN MAH HEID.

HELP! IT'LL STING ME.

BUZZZZZ

HUH! THAT'S YOUR FAT FRIEND IN THERE.

BOB'S AN OOT O' CONTROL ROBOT NOW.

BUZZZZZ

EEK! I'M RUNNIN' HAME.

CLUNK!

OOYAH!

I'LL HAE TAE STAND. BOB'S NO' BACK WI' MAH BUCKET YET.

THE BUCKET CAPTURES WULLIE'S DUG, AND CLOUTS BIG ERCHIE ON THE LUG.

WHAT'S MISSING?

MAH BUCKET! IT'S BLAWN AWA' IN THIS GALE.

THERE IT GOES.

GOT YE AT LAST.

MICHTY! IT'S ALIVE!

GOTCHA WI' MAH RUGBY TACKLE.

IT'S HARRY. MAH BUCKET MUST HAE LANDED ON HIM.

YOU STAY!

YOU HAME!

SULK!

OCH, NO! THE WIND'S CAUGHT MAH BUCKET AGAIN.

CLANG!

HOWL!

BIG ERCHIE McGRAW.

DANGEROUS FLIPPIN THING!

MAH BUCKET.

IT'S STUCK ON THE FLYER'S LUM.

PLOP!

AUCHENSHOOGLE STEAM RAILWAY.

WOOOF!

IT'S POPPED OFF AND THE WIND'S REALLY CAUGHT THIS TIME.

IT'S GONE FOR GOOD, HARRY. I'LL SHARE YOUR BED TILL I GET A NEW ANE.

THERE'S NAE CHANCE THAT HARRY WILL PASS,
WULLIE'S DOG TRAINING CLASS.

I NEED TO DO SOME ROAD WORK BEFORE THE KILTWALK NEXT WEEKEND.

NOT FOR MYSELF BUT I'M TAKING HARRY WITH ME. HE'S DOING THE WOOF WALK.

I'M INVENTING A SUPER ENERGY DRINK FOR HIM, WITH ADDED PORRIDGE.

HE LIKES IT ONYWAY.

LOOK AT HIM GO - I MIGHT MAKE A FORTUNE WI' THIS POTION FOR LAZY DOGS.

I CAN HARDLY KEEP UP WI' HIM.

YOU'RE DAFT, ECK. YOU'LL NEVER MANAGE TO DRAG THAT LUMP ROUND THE KILTWALK ROUTE.

I'M TAKING BRUNO ON THE WOOF WALK BUT HE ONLY HAS ONE SPEED - STOP.

PULL!

MY POTION'S A FAILURE - HARRY HAS RUN OUT O' STEAM ALREADY.

PECH!

JINGS! I HOPE THIS DISNAE HAPPEN TO WEE ECK.

HE'LL NEVER LIFT BRUNO, NEVER MIND CARRY HIM HAME.

ZZZZ

HELP MAH BOAB!

IT'S WEE ECK THAT'S RUN OUT OF STEAM AND BRUNO HAS CARRIED HIM HAME.

ZZZZZZ!

WELL, THAT WAS A BRAW WALK, WULLIE.

WALK? WALK? YE SLEPT THROUGH MOST O' IT.

WULLIE'S AWA' TO BED EARLY!

ZZZZZZ

OOR LADDIE IS FITTER THAN MOST,
AND NOW HE'S TRAINING 'THE SUNDAY POST'.

A HIGH THING LIKE A CLIMBING WALL, DISNAE BOTHER OOR WULLIE AT ALL.

BOB AND ME ARE GOING TAE THE AUCHENSHOOGLE CLIMBING WALL.

LOOK FOR THE HANDHOLDS AND FOOTHOLDS.

THIS IS EASY! I'VE BEEN CLIMBIN' SINCE BEFORE I COULD WALK.

HOI!

PULL!

OUT OF MY WAY, SHRIMP. WE'RE PROPER CLIMBERS.

MICHTY!

WE'RE NO' PLAYING LIKE YOU LADDIES. WE'RE CLIMBING BEN STOORIE TOMORROW.

HUH! ME AND MY PAL WILL RACE YOU TAE THE TOP.

YOU'LL NEED A CRANE TO GET LARD BOY HERE UP THE MOUNTAIN.

PROD!

I'M NO' CLIMBIN' WITH BOB. I'M CLIMBIN' WITH BILLY.

WHATEVER! YOU'LL HAVE NO CHANCE.

NEXT DAY-

WHAT KEPT YE? WE'VE STARTED.

CARRY ON! WE'LL OVERTAKE YOU IN MINUTES, SONNY.

OH YEAH? MY PAL BILLY'S A BRAW CLIMBER.

PULL!

WOW!

PUFF! PANT!

AT LAST! I WAS NEAR FALLIN' ASLEEP.

WHERE'S YOUR PAL? HE MUST BE A WONDER CLIMBER.

HE GOT FED UP WAITIN' ON YE.

SO HE'S HAVIN' HIS LUNCH ON A GRASSY BIT OWER THERE.

A GOAT!

AYE, BILLY LIVES ON BEN STOORIE. HE'S UP AND DOON IT TEN TIMES A DAY.

HA! HA! BILLY WASN'T THE ONLY GOAT ON BEN STOORIE!

UNUSUAL FOR OOR RASCALLY BOY, HIS HAIR IS WULLIE'S PRIDE AND JOY.

SOAPY AND BOB ARE VISITING WULLIE.

MICHTY! SOAPY NEVER WEARS A HAT.

MY DAD GOT NEW HAIR CLIPPERS FOR CHRISTMAS.

HE'S BEEN TRYING THEM OUT ON ME.

HA! HA! YOU COULD GET A PART IN A ZOMBIE MOVIE.

MY SISTER CUT MY HAIR WHILE I WAS HAVING A WEE SNOOZE.

WHAT A PAIR OF SLAP HEADS!

I'LL NEVER CHANGE MY BONNIE SPIKY HAIR. IT'S AS MUCH A PART OF ME AS MY DUNGAREES.

THEN-

HELP MAH BOAB! THE WIND'S CAUGHT MY TENNER.

WATCH ME SPEAR THIS BIT OF PAPER.

HERE, THAT'S NO ORDINARY PIECE OF PAPER.

NO, IT'S MY CASH - THANK GOODNESS FOR THAT SPIKY HEAD. HERE'S A WEE REWARD.

THANKS, P.C. MURDOCH.

I'VE BOUGHT US ALL SOME BUBBLEGUM TO CHEER YOU BALDIES UP.

LET'S SEE WHO CAN BLOW THE BIGGEST BUBBLE.

MINE IS GETTING THE BIGGEST.

YOU'VE A LOT MORE HOT AIR IN YOU THAN SOAPY.

THIS IS GOING TO BE A RECORD BREAKER.

OCH! YOU'VE BURST IT WITH YOUR SPIKY NAPPER.

POP!

HA! HA! IT LOOKS LIKE YOU'VE A BIG BALD SPOT, WULLIE.

AW,NO! MY BONNIE HAIR!

MA HAD TO CUT THE BUBBLEGUM OUT. SHE COULD GET A JOB SHEARING SHEEP.

WULLIE PLANS TAE RIDE A DERBY WINNER,
PITY THE CUDDY IS NEEDING ITS DINNER.

I'M TRYING TO LOOK TALLER.

I'M FED UP BEING WEE. FOWK LAUGH AT ME FOR BEING WEE.

DON'T BE DAFT, WULLIE. LOTS O' SPORTSMEN ARE WEE. THE BEST JOCKEYS ARE ALL SMALL.

I CAN JUST SEE MYSELF WINNING THE DERBY.

HUH! I'VE ONLY THIS AULD TOY HORSE TO PRACTISE ON.

PLAYING ON A TOY HORSE AT YOUR AGE, WULLIE? TIME YOU GREW UP.

OCH, SHUT UP, GINGER TAIT!

WAIT A MINUTE. PRIMROSE HAS A PONY SHE MIGHT LEND ME - IF I WAS NICE TO HER.

HELLO, PRIMROSE. WOULD ONE CARE FOR A HALF-SOOKED SOOR PLOOM?

HOW KIND OF YOU, WILLIAM.

WELL, US HORSEY TYPES SHOULD STICK TOGETHER.

YOU LIKE HORSES, WILLIAM? YOU MUST TRY MY PONY, ISLA.

YOU CAN'T SIT ON A HORSE WITH ALL THE JUNK YOU KEEP IN YOUR POCKETS.

GIVE IT HERE AND I'LL PUT IT IN MY BAG.

THANKS, PRIMROSE.

CATAPULT, CONKERS, WATER PISTOL, CHEWING GUM, KEYS AND AN APPLE.

APPLE? BRAW!

ISLA! YOU'RE TEARING MY BAG.

CRUNCH

NEVER MIND YOUR BAG - WHAT ABOOT MY APPLE?

BOYS! ALL YOU CAN THINK ABOUT IS YOURSELVES.

HOWL!

WHACK!

I'VE GROWN TWO INCHES WI' THIS BUMP ON MY HEAD.

PRIMROSE HAD A HORSESHOE IN HER BAG.

WULLIE'S NEW BOOTS HAVE NOT ONE SCRATCH, SO HE CAN'T PLAY IN THE FITBA MATCH.

WHAUR'S AUCHENSHOOGLE? I HAVEN'T A CLUE,
BUT IT'S CERTAINLY SCOTTISH THROUGH AND THROUGH.

THE FARMER CAN'T BELIEVE HIS EYES,
WI' HIS AULD SHEEP WULLIE'S WON A PRIZE.

WULLIE'S ACCIDENTAL STUMBLE,
PUTS AN END TAE TUMMY RUMBLE.

IS THERE ANY STRANGER CREATURE, THAN OOR WULLIE'S POSH NEW TEACHER?

WE'VE GOT A NEW TEACHER AND SHE'S AWFY POSH.

WILLIAM, WHAT IS SRI LANKA'S MAJOR EXPORT?

I DINNAE KEN, MISS.

I TAKE IT THAT MEANS YOU DON'T KNOW? IN CLASS YOU REALLY MUST SPEAK PROPER ENGLISH.

WHIT?

AT PLAYTIME...

GIES A KICK O' THE BA', SOAPY.

WILLIAM!

DIDN'T YOU LISTEN TO A THING I SAID ABOUT SPEAKING PROPER ENGLISH? SEE ME AFTER SCHOOL.

YOU SAID I HAD TAE SPEAK PROPERLY IN CLASS - BUT I'M NO' IN CLASS, I'M OOTSIDE.

AFTER SCHOOL...

ARE YOU GOING TO GIVE ME HARD SUMS TO DO AS PUNISHMENT?

NO, I'D LIKE YOU TO CARRY MY BAG TO MY NEW COTTAGE.

JINGS! WHAT'S THIS? ARE YE TEACHER'S PET NOW, WULLIE?

IGNORE HIM, WILLIAM.

A LOCAL WORKMAN IS DOING UP MY COTTAGE AND I CAN'T UNDERSTAND A WORD HE'S SAYING. YOU KNOW ALL THE SCOTS WORDS SO WILL YOU HELP ME OUT, PLEASE?

YOU WANT ME TO BE YOUR INTERPRETER? NAE BOTHER.

AYE, LASS. YOUR GUTTERS WERE BARKIT SO I HOWKED OOT A' THE GLAUR. THEN I MENDED YOUR DYKE WHAUR THE FERMER'S STIRKS HAD LOWPED OWER AND COWPED IT DOON.

NOT ONE WORD.

WILLIAM? PLEASE?

THE WORKMAN HAS CLEANED YOUR RONE PIPES AND THEN HE REPAIRED THE WALL THAT SOME OF YOUR NEIGHBOUR'S COWS HAD KNOCKED OVER.

DID I NO' JIST SAY A' THAT?

THANK YOU SO MUCH, WILLIAM. I DID SOME BAKING LAST NIGHT. YOU CAN HAVE SOME AS A THANK YOU.

BRAW.

JINGS. SHE'S NO' BAD AFTER ALL. WHO WOULD HAE THOUGHT IT?

FOR A TEACHER SHE DISNAE KNOW MUCH, BUT SHE'LL IMPROVE WI' A FEW LESSONS - BUT MICHTY, SHE'S A BRAW BAKER. MMMM.

WULLIE STARTS TAE DAE SOME JOKING,
BY HANDING OOT AN AWFY SOAKING.

I'M GOING TAE BE REAL CHEERY TODAY.

'YOUR HEALTH' IN THE POST SAYS LAUGHING COULD MAKE YOU LIVE LONGER.

ANE OF THESE LADS IS READING AN AWFY SERIOUS PAPER. THE OTHER ANE IS READING THE BEANO.

SHARE PRICES FELL AGAIN. LIFE'S NO' WORTH LIVING.

HA! HA! DENNIS THE MENACE WILL KEEP ME SMILING A' DAY.

AYE, THE SUNDAY POST IS RIGHT!

THERE'S AULD EASTON - HE'S ALWAYS FRETTING ABOUT HIS FLOOERS. I'LL GIVE HIM A LAUGH.

DAE YOU LIKE MY FLOWER, MR EASTON?

WHIT KIND IS IT, WULLIE?

A WATER LILY! HA! HA!

YOU FEEL BETTER IF YOU HAE A LAUGH.

IS THAT SO?

HA! HA! YOU'RE RIGHT, WULLIE. I FEEL BETTER NOW.

HOWL!

YOU SAID LAUGHTER'S THE BEST MEDICINE. DAE YOU NO' LIKE THE TASTE O' YOUR OWN MEDICINE, LADDIE?

HELP MAH BOAB! I'M WRINGING.

THIS ROAD ROLLER WILL PRESS MY DUNGAREES DRY.

IT WORKED - THEY'RE WARM AND DRY. I SHOULD GET MA ANE O' THESE THINGS.

WULLIE, YOU'VE GOT A GREAT DOD O' TAR STUCK TO YOUR BAHOOCHIE.

I THOUGHT MY DUNGAREES WERE HEAVY.

I'D BETTER HURRY HOME, BOB. I CANNAE TARRY HERE WITH YOU.

TARRY? DID YOU GET IT, BOB? WHAT A BRAW LAUGH.

YOU'RE NUTS!

SLAP!

AT HAME-

WHAT'S UP, MR HAPPY? YOU WERE GOING TO BE LAUGHING A' DAY TODAY.

MY HANDS ARE GLUED TAE MY TARRY BOTTOM.

HA! HA! HA! HA! HEE! HEE! THAT'S PRICELESS!

STUCK!

SOME FOWK WILL LAUGH AT ANYTHING. NAE WONDER MA'S SO HEALTHY.

THE WILD LADDIES CAN HAVE A BALL,
AUCHENSHOOGLE HAS NO LAW AT ALL.

WULLIE HAS A PLAN TO HATCH,
IF HE'S TO SEE THE SCOTLAND MATCH.

FRIDAY PAST —

WISH I HAD A TICKET FOR THE SCOTLAND WALES WORLD CUP MATCH TONIGHT.

HEY, WILLIAM — COME AND MEET MY PAL, LORI MEIKLEJOHN. YOU'LL NOT KNOW HER, SHE GOES TO CRAIGMONT SCHOOL.

HI LORI — I'M WULLIE, ONLY PAN LOAF PRIMROSE CALLS ME WILLIAM.

WE'RE GOING SKATING.

ONLY FOR A LITTLE WHILE. I'VE TO LOOK AFTER MY WEE BROTHER WHILE DAD GETS READY FOR HAMPDEN TONIGHT.

HE DISNAE HAVE ONY SPARE TICKETS, YOUR DAD?

AYE, HE DOES ACTUALLY.

YOU LASSIES TAKE YOUR TIME AT THE SKATING. I'LL GO AND MIND YER WEE BROTHER FOR YE.

HELLO, IWONA. I'M HERE INSTEAD O' LORI TAE MIND THE WEE MAN.

OOR WULLIE? THIS IS VERY GOOD OF YOU. ALEKS HERE WAS WANTING TO PLAY FOOTBALL BUT IT'S RAINING.

TIME WULLIE TAUGHT YE ANOTHER GREAT SCOTTISH GAME, ALEKS.

LOBBY FITBA — YE NEED TO KNOW THIS GAME BECAUSE IT'S AYE RAINING HERE.

THUMP!

GOOO-AAAL! LOBBY FLOORS ARE GREAT FOR SLIDING ON TO CELEBRATE A GOAL.

GOAL, IS IT? THAT'S A GOOD OMEN FOR TONIGHT.

GOOO-AAAL!

HI, MR MEIKLEJOHN. I HEAR YOU'RE A' GOING TO THE MATCH TONIGHT.

BUY SOME TREATS FOR WATCHING THE MATCH ON THE BOX TONIGHT, WULLIE.

AYE, WATCHING IT ON TELLY IS NO' AS GOOD AS REALLY BEING AT THE MATCH.

I'VE GOT A SPARE TICKET, IF YOU'D LIKE IT.

HAVE YOU REALLY? WELL, FANCY THAT. AYE, I'LL TAKE IT.

COME ON, SCOTLAND!

JINGS! WE LOST. BUT THAT DOESN'T GET SCOTS DOON. THERE'S AYE THE NEXT GAME.

EDITOR'S NOTE — TWO GARETH BALE GOALS FOR WALES PUT PAID TO SCOTLAND'S WORLD CUP 2014 QUALIFYING HOPES

WULL THINKS HIS BOOTS ARE NO FUN, UNTIL OOR SCAMP IS ON THE RUN.

HAVING SUCH A FLY WEE LAD,
HELPS WULLIE'S DEAR OLD DAD.

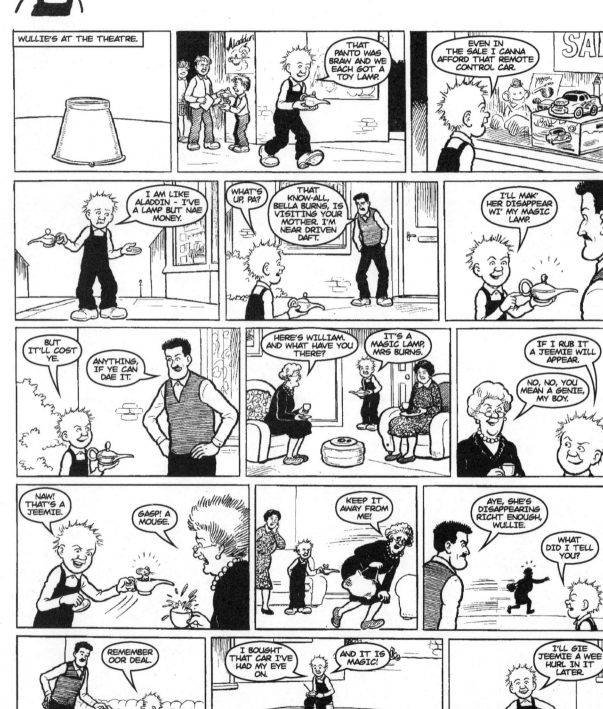

OOR WULLIE STARTS TAE WONDER,
IF APPLES HE'LL GET TAE PLUNDER.

**WULLIE'S HEADING FOR DETENTION,
FOR HE WISNAE PAYING ATTENTION.**

WULLIE'S IN SCHOOL.

LOTS OF BEAUTIFUL THINGS ARE BLUE, LIKE THE SKY AND THE OCEAN. FOR HOMEWORK I WANT YOU TO WRITE A POEM ABOUT SOMETHING BLUE.

OOR LITTLE BOY BLUE IS ASLEEP.

ZZZZZ

RING!!!

TIME FOR HAME.

COME ON, YOU LAZY BOYS! STOP DAWDLIN'.

HA! HA! YOU'RE AYE FIRST OOT THE DOOR.

DID YOU HEAR WHAT MISS SAID FOR OOR HOMEWORK, WULLIE?

OF COURSE! I WAS ONLY PRETENDIN' TAE SLEEP.

AYE, RIGHT! YOU WERE PRETENDIN' TAE SNORE AS WELL.

I'M GREAT AT WRITIN' POEMS. THIS'LL BE EASY-PEASY!

WAIT, WAIT... HERE'S ANE COMING INTAE MY HEAD NOW.

OCH! IT PASSED RICHT THROUGH WITHOOT STOPPING.

AHA! I'VE THOUGHT UP A BRAW ANE.

NEXT DAY.

YOU CAN START, PRIMROSE.

I LIKE TO LOOK AT THE BLUE, BLUE SKY, UP IN THE AIR SO VERY HIGH. I WISH I HAD A BLOUSE THAT COLOUR, BUT I'VE NOT, MINE IS DULLER.

I PICKED THE FLOOERS O' BONNY BLUE, AND FED THEM TAE TAM SCOBIE'S COO.

SIGH!

AND WILLIAM.

I MICHT HAVE GOT A BITTY MIXED UP, MISS.

I TOOK MY HANKY FRAE MY POCKET, AND FOUND THAT IT WAS REALLY MAWKIT. BUT A SNOTTERY NOSE YOU CANNAE LEAVE, SO I BLEW IT ON MY SLEEVE.

REALLY!

WE WERE TALKING ABOUT THE COLOUR BLUE BUT YOU WERE ASLEEP.

AYE, MISS.

I REALLY BLEW IT! I GOT A HUNDRED LINES. I MUST NOT SLEEP IN CLASS.

IN THE BURN THERE'S BONNY TROOT,
AND WULLIE PLANS TAE FISH THEM OOT.

THIS HALLOWEEN WILL BE GREAT FUN, WITH ONE FOR ALL AND ALL FOR ONE.

THE BOYS ARE COMING ROOND TAE MAK' PLANS FOR HALLOWEEN.

WE NEED TAE DECIDE ON GUISIN' COSTUMES FOR THIS YEAR.

WE ALWAYS DAE THINGS TOGETHER SO WHY DON'T WE GO AS THE THREE MUSKETEERS?

AYE - ANE FOR ALL AND ALL FOR ANE!

HIGH FIVES!

LATER-

WE'LL GO TAE THE EASTONS' HOOSE FIRST. THEY LIKE HAVIN' GUISERS.

WE'RE HERE TAE RIGHT ONY WRONGS - APART FROM HAMEWORK THAT IS.

MICHTY! FAT BOB IS LIGHT ON HIS FEET.

THEY LADDIES HAE AYE BEEN LIKE THE THREE MUSKETEERS.

THAT WAS RARE FUN, BOYS. HERE'S SOMETHING FOR YOUR GOODY BAG.

YOU ARE ZE OWER KIND, MADAM.

NEXT HOOSE-

I'LL HOLD THIS VILLAIN PRISONER WHILE YOU ESCAPE, MY QUEEN.

HA! HA! I MICHT NIP DOON TAE THE BINGO FOR A WHILE.

YOU'RE A BUNCH O' WEE CHARMERS. HAVE SOME HAME MADE PIES AND SWEETS.

FAIR THEE WELL, BEAUTIFUL LADY.

THAT'S BEEN RARE FUN GUISIN' TOGETHER.

AYE, NOTHING WILL EVER SPLIT US UP.

WHAT A HAUL THIS YEAR. THERE'S PLENTY FOR ALL O' US.

LEAVE SOME O' MRS YOUNGER'S APPLE PIES FOR US, BOB.

OKAY, BUT WHERE'S A' THE CASH WE GOT?

ARE YOU SAYIN' I'M A THIEF?

IF THE CAP FITS WEAR IT.

YOUR POCKETS ARE JINGLING TAE, BOB.

WOLLOP!

BANG!

YOU'RE A BIG FIBBER!

AM NOT!

YE BOTH ARE!

THUMP!

PULL!

WHACK!

WE'RE NO' TALKING NOW. BUT AT LEAST WE'RE A' BASHED TOGETHER.

AN AULD SHIRT IN YER FACE,
CAN SEND YE A' OWER THE PLACE.

WULLIE!

THAT'S MA.

TAKE THESE OLD CLOTHES TAE THE JUMBLE SALE. THEY'RE RAISING FUNDS FOR A HALLOWEEN TREAT FOR THE OLD FOLK.

I'LL TAKE THEM ON MY CARTIE.

BUT—

I CANNA SEE WHAUR I'M GOING FOR THIS SHIRT.

JINGS! IT'S GETTING WORSE AND I'VE NAE BRAKES.

SORRY I'M LATE FOR THE SALE BUT I ENDED UP A MILE OOT O' TOWN AND CLOTHES ALL OWER THE PLACE.

THE SALE'S FINISHED, BUT NEVER MIND, WULLIE.

MA'LL BE DISAPPOINTED HER CLOTHES DIDNAE HELP CHEER UP THE OLD FOWK.

AUCHENSHOOGLE RETIREMENT HOME.

I'VE GOT A RARE PLAN BOB – BUT I NEED YOUR HELP.

I'M UP FOR ONYTHING, WULLIE.

WULLIE AND BOB'S THEATRE ARE GOING TO PERFORM A DAY IN THE LIFE O' AUCHENSHOOGLE.

WHAT RARE! I DINNA GET INTO AUCHENSHOOGLE ANY MORE.

KIND POLIS MAN, WILL YOU HELP ME ACROSS THE STREET?

AYE, YOU'LL BE SAFE WITH ME, WIFIE.

STEP THIS WAY – I'LL HAUD UP THE TRAFFIC.

HA! HA! FAT BOB'S PC MURDOCH.

YOU'RE MORE NEEDING TAE HAUD UP YOUR TROOSERS.

EEK! THE POLIS BREEKS.

SHRIEK! HA! HA!

THAT WAS RARE FUN, LADDIES.

CACKLE!

JUST LIKE MURDOCH IN HIS YOUNG DAY.

HAUDS UP THE TRAFFIC BUT NO' HIS BREEKS. HA! HA!

DID YE GET THE CLOTHES TAE THE SALE?

I CAN HONESTLY SAY THE CLOTHES HELPED CHEER UP THE OLD FOLK.

WE'RE THE BOYS.

WE DIDNAE TELL ONY LIES.

MONSTERS AND MUMMIES ON THE STREET,
MEANS HALLOWEEN AND TRICK OR TREAT.

PLAYING FITBA IN THE PARK,
ISN'T FUN WHEN IT'S TOO DARK.

WILL THE SPOOK O' STOORIE GLEN,
MAKE HER APPEARANCE AGAIN?

WULLIE'S GOING TAE TAKE SOME CHANCES,
TAE IMPROVE HIS POCKET FINANCES.

I'M AYE BROKE.

WE'RE GOING TO SELL FRESHLY SQUEEZED JUICE TO TOURISTS.

JINGS! THAT'S NOT A BAD IDEA, PRIMROSE.

DO YOU WANT A SQUEEZE TOO, WILLIAM?

GET AWAY, WOMAN. YOU'RE FRESHER THAN YOUR JUICE.

WONDER WHAT I COULD MAKE TO SELL TO TOURISTS?

MAKE SOME BISCUITS IN THE OVEN AND SELL THEM.

COULD DO, I SUPPOSE.

BUT NAW! FAT BOB WOULD EAT ALL MY PROFITS.

MUNCH!

TOURISTS LIKE PLATES WITH PLACE NAMES ON THEM. AND I'VE GOT ALL THIS AULD MODELLING CLAY.

I'M NO' BAD AT MAKING PLATES - SORT OF.

AND I'LL WRITE AUCHENSHOOGLE WI' THE WEE LETTERS OFF THE FRIDGE.

AUCHEN

SOON-

THAT'S ME IN BUSINESS.

PLATES CHEEP

YOU'LL NEVER SELL THESE AWFUL THINGS, WILLIAM. THEY'RE ALL WOBBLY.

I KEN THAT.

THAT'S PART O' MY MARKETING PLAN.

WOBBLE!

GENUINE SHOOGLY PLATES FRAE AUCHENSHOOGLE.

WOBBLE!

THAT'S SO CUTE. I'LL TAKE TWO PLEASE.

BUSINESS NOT GOOD, GIRLS? HERE, LET ME BUY A BOTTLE O' YOUR JUICE WITH MY SALES MONEY.

STOP BRAGGING, WILLIAM.

GUGGS! THEIR JUICE IS NAE BETTER THAN MY PLATES.

TASTY CHIPS WERE WULL'S DOWNFALL, NOW HE CANNA SEE MUCH AT ALL.

A UNIFORM THAT BARES WULLIE'S KNEES, WILL NEVER BEAT HIS DUNGAREES.

THE FANS HAVE STARTED FIGHTING, OWER THE STAR'S AWFY WRITING.

WULLIE HAS NO TIME FOR A BATH,
A SECOND ONE CAUSES HIM SOME WRATH.

WULLIE'S IN THE BATH.

ACH! WHAT A PLESTER A BATH IS.

OH, WILLIAM. I LIKE A MAN WHO TAKES CARE OF HIS APPEARANCE.

THAT'S ME, PRIMROSE.

TRY MY NEW COLOGNE, IT'S FOR GIRLS AND BOYS.

BUT NO FOR BOB OR SOAPY. THEY'LL CALL ME SAFT.

TELL THE TEACHER I'LL BE A WEE BIT LATE.

ANOTHER BATH TAE WASH THON PONG AWA'.

SHORTLY-

HAVE YOU FINISHED YOUR HISTORY PROJECT, WILLIAM?

NO' YET, MISS. TOMORROW WITHOUT FAIL.

AFTER SCHOOL-

COME UP TO PEATY POND WITH ME, WILLIAM.

ARE YE TRYING TAE CATCH PUDDOCKS?

NO, WE'LL COLLECT MUD THAT WILL BE GOOD FOR OUR SKIN.

WHIT?

WOWP!

YOU MAY BE UNCOMFORTABLE BUT YOUR SKIN WILL BENEFIT, WILLIAM.

I'M DROOKIT, YE DAFT GOWK.

IN FACT THINGS CANNAE GET MUCH WORSE.

REMEMBER YOUR HISTORY PROJECT.

HUMPH! I SPOKE TOO SOON.

WAIT A MEENIT! I'LL GET MY BOATS AND DAE MY HISTORY IN THE BATH.

THE QUESTION IS - HOW DID THE SPANISH ARMADA NO' SEE SIR FRANCIS DRAKE?

EASY! THEY COULDNAE SEE ROOND THE GIANT RUBBER DUCK. HA! HA!

WHIT RARE FUN A BATH IS!

THOUGH IT'S NO' DECEMBER ONE,
WULLIE'S HAVIN' ADVENT FUN.

WULLIE SWINGS HIS SWORD WI' POWER, BUT IT TURNS HIM INTAE A FLOWER.

SNOW BOARDING DOON THE HILL,
DISNAE GIVE WULL'S MA A THRILL.

WINTER ARRIVES IN AUCHENSHOOGLE.

SNAW! STAV'S FORECAST WAS RICHT.

DOUBLE HELPING O' THICK PORRIDGE TAE KEEP OOT THE COLD.

I'LL FETCH BOB AND SOAPY FOR THE FIRST SLEDGING O' THE YEAR.

WHAT ARE YOU DOING WI' THAT THING, WULLIE?

EH?

EVERYBODY USES SNOWBOARDS TODAY.

I KEN THAT.

I WAS THINKING O' TAKING THIS TAE THE ANTIQUE ROADSHOW.

AYE, RIGHT. YOU'VE NO' GOT A SNOWBOARD.

SHOVE!

DO TOO! I'LL MEET YE ON BINKIE BRAE WI' IT.

SOON-

THAT LOOKS LIKE WULLIE AT THE TOP O' THE HILL.

EAT SLUSH, SUCKERS! WULLIE'S ON HIS SNOWBOARD.

HE HAS A SNOWBOARD.

AND HE'S GUID ON IT.

WHAT A SPEED DEMON. HE'S GOIN' REALLY FAST.

AYE, AND I WISH I WASNAE. I DINNA KEN HOW TAE STOP.

WHUMFF!!

I'M WET AND FREEZIN' AND I'M GOING BACK TAE MY GUID AULD SLEDGE.

TAKE AFF THEY WET DUNGAREES WHILE I IRON YOU A SPARE PAIR.

I DINNA THINK SO, MA.

MY IRONING BOARD. WULLIE! A WORD WI' YE.

WULLIE'S HOPIN' MA THAWS OOT BEFORE THE SNOW.

I'M GROUNDED!

WULL'S PAL IS LOST IN THE SNAW, AND WON'T BE FOUND UNTIL A THAW.

SOAPY THINKS THE FIGHT'S UNFAIR,
WHEN SNOWBALLS FLY OUT OF THIN AIR.

AUCHENSHOOGLE'S GOT SNOW.

WULLIE'S MADE A BRAW SNOWMAN.

BUT WHAUR IS THE LAD HIMSELF?

WULLIE, COME ON OOT!

SPLAT!

URF!

FUNNY! THERE'S NAEBODY AROOND.

NO' AGAIN! WHA'S DOIN' THIS?

I'LL MOLLY - KATE YE WHEN I FIND YE.

IT WAS ME, SOAPY.

YIKES! THE SNOWMAN'S HAUNTED.

IT'S A BRAW DISGUISE, IS IT NO'? I MADE IT OOT O' COTTON WOOL – ALTHOUGH THE CARROT WAS JEEMY'S.

HAW! HAW! THAT'S BRILLIANT, WULLIE.

I'M WAITIN' FOR PC MURDOCH DOING HIS ROONDS. THEN I'M GOING TAE BLAST HIS POLIS BUNNET.

I'LL STAY AND WATCH.

SOAPY'S HANDS ARE EMPTY AND WULLIE IS NOWHERE TAE BE SEEN. LOOKS LIKE I'M SAFE.

WRONG, PC MURDOCH!

THAT'S NO' POSSIBLE - THE SNOWBALL JUST VAPOURISED.

WHAT'S NO' POSSIBLE IS A TALKING SNOWMAN.

BUT HOW DID MY SNOWBALL NO' HIT YE?

I'M WEARING MY BIG AULD HELMET SO THAT I CAN KEEP A HOT WATER BOTTLE INSIDE IT. BRAW TAE HAVE A WARM HEID.

SO MY SNOWBALL MELTED.

'SNOW' FAIR!

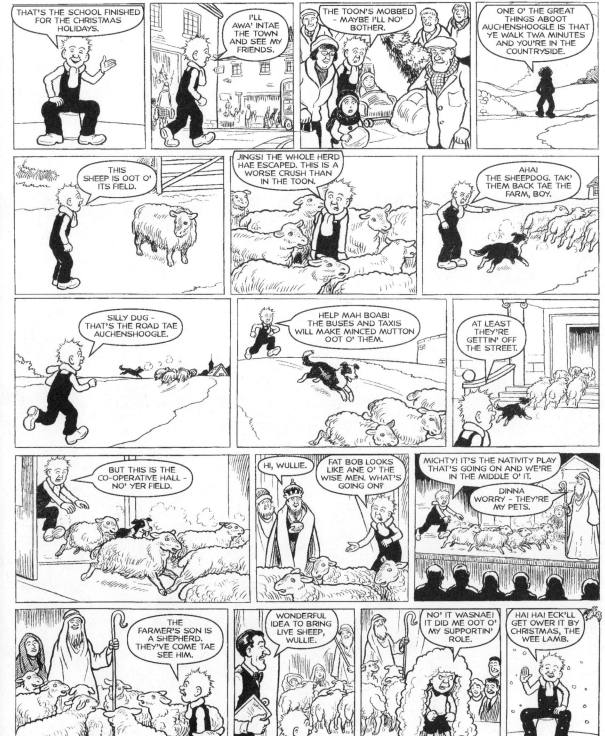

IT'S A SHOCK, AS YOU'LL SEE,
WULLIE FINDS A TALKING TREE.

I'M LOOKING FORWARD TAE DECORATING THE CHRISTMAS TREE TONIGHT.

WE'LL NEED TAE GET ONE FIRST.

MY PAL CHRIS PATON THE FORESTER SAID WE COULD CUT A REAL TREE.

CHRIS IS GOING TAE MEET US HERE.

I'M GOING TAE TRY A FEW PRACTICE CHOPS.

WHOA! THAT TREE IS OWER BROAD TAE GET IN THE DOOR.

HERE'S ANE THAT'S BEEN TO SCOTTISH SLIMMERS.

EEK! IT SPOKE!

PLEASE DON'T CHOP ME.

CHRIS WAS HIDIN' BEHIND THE TREE. HE WAS AYE A JOKER.

DID I FLEG YE, WULLIE?

NAW!

THIS IS THE TREE I PICKED OOT FOR YE. CAN YE FELL IT, WULLIE?

AS LONG AS IT DISNAE SPEAK BACK TAE ME.

TIMBER!

YOU CANNA GET A TREE MUCH FRESHER THAN THAT.

IT'LL BE HEAVY TAE CARRY, WULLIE.

NOTHIN' TAE US LUMBERJACKS.

YOU'RE A STRONG WEE LADDIE.

PUFF! AYE, GASP!

NOW A' YOU HAVE TO DO IS FILL ONE O' YOUR AULD BUCKETS WITH EARTH AND PLANT IT.

NAE BOTHER. PECH!

GETTING EARTH IS NO' SAE EASY. THE GROUND IS FROZEN SOLID.

SHORTLY-

COME ON THEN, WULLIE. YOU CAN DECORATE THE TREE NOW.

AW! OOR WEE LUMBERJACK HAS CONKED OOT.

ZZZZZZ!

SOUNDS LIKE HE'S SAWING WOOD.

THE TREE CAN WAIT TILL TOMORROW.

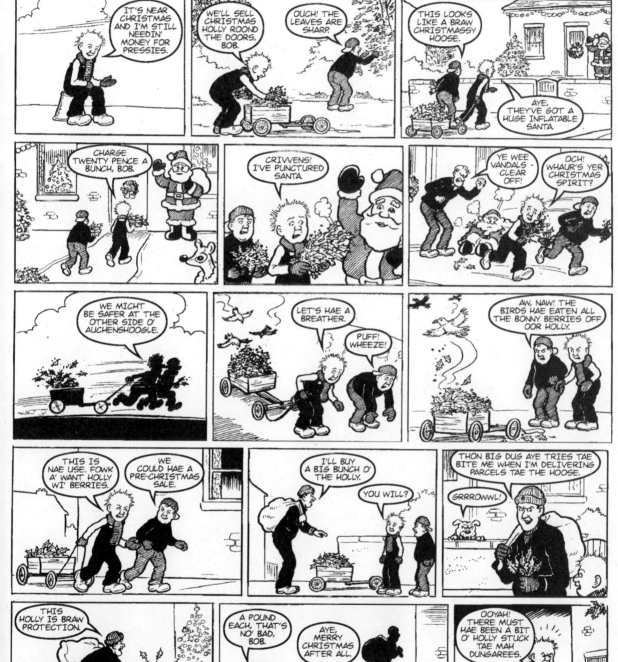

USING WULLIE'S MUSICAL EAR,
HERE'S A GRAND WAY TAE END THE YEAR.